AMAZON
★ ★ ★ ★ ★
Review Club

Ken Rochon, Jr., Ph.D.

Amazon 5 Star Review Club

ISBN: 978-1-64810-109-0

Printed in the United States of America

'You will be the same person in five years as you are today except for the people you meet and the books you read.'

~ Charlie 'Tremendous' Jones

Acknowledgements

To my son Kenny who inspires me everyday to make his life better with books like this to guide him to more abundance and wisdom.

To my wife Nelly who was there cheering me on when I wrote my first book in 2009. This started it all.

To my partners in publishing, Al Granger, Carolyn Sheltraw, and Joyce White for their commitment to creating legacy worthy works of wisdom.

• • • • •

To my dad, George White, Sr., my life-long mentor who was and is ever present for me with his loving, determined and passionate spirit.

To my children and large extended families of children that have inspired me to grow in ways my finite mind could never have imagined.

To Ken Rochon, with whom I spent many hours as an ambassador for the Perfect Networker platform, and for including my contributions into his first book..which started it all.

To my God, immediate and extended families, multitudes of my students of all ages, colleagues, personal and professional partners, and mentors, who have all influenced my perception of life to understand that the thorns on the stem of any rose are essential to the stem. The thorns provide the strength for the weight of the rosebud to blossom. Only then does the world experience the rose in its full beauty when the sweet fragrance is given away.

• • • • •

To Jeff Spenard, Robert Ciolino, Ryan Treasure, Geetha Krishnan, Sharon Frame and the Voice America Live Radio Team that makes my show 'AmpLIFiEd' Radio Show a platform that serves authors and leaders like the ones featured in this book.

To Alicia Couri, Anna Renault, Belinda Fraley Huesman, Chris & Lorissa Naugle, Courtney A. Bradley, Christoff Weihman, Dr. Dan Amzallag, Dr. Emily Letran, Fantastic Frank Johnson, Gayela Bynum, Jackie Gardner, Joe Frazzette, Kayvon, Matt Belair, Marcia Merrill, Melissa Hull Gallemore, Melinda Curle, Meleny Inspires Thomas, Dr. Molly Casey, Rich Wilens, Robert Johnson, Sandy Lynch, Dr. Sarah Langley, Steven Macalester, Sylvia Henderson, T. Allen Hanes, Todd Thomas, Victor Pierantoni for believing in the Perfect Publishing Social Proof Viral Campaign Technology.

To Adam Brian Giandomenico, AJ Puedan, Alex Lowy, Alexey Koyfman, Andrea Adams-Miller, Barry Shore, Becca Tebon, Bill Walsh, Charles Byrd, Cheryl Brenner, Dave Conklin, David Cavanagh, David Corbin, David Richardson, Doug Sandler, Ernesto Verdugo, Federico Giller, Frank Shankwitz, Glen Ledwell, Glenn Dietzel, Gordon Thorn, Greg Jacobson, Greg Reid, Jason Myers, Jeremy Hess, John Duffy, Justin Lafazan, Kate Lemburg, Keith Leon, Ken Krell, Ken McArthur, Kennedy Gilbertson, Lee-Ann Fullard, Captain Lou Edwards, Max Major, Michael Wong, Moh Ducis, Orly Amor, Nadine Molas, Paula Fellingham, Peter Anthony Wynn, Phil Randazzo, Rebecca Ramirez, Rick Frishman, Rick Lewis, Roger Salam, Sarah Coolidge, Sean Patrick McCullough, Sima Patel, Steve Greenspan, Steve McAdams, Terry Brennan, Tim Konig, Timothy R. Johnson, Tony Kosack, Tonya Hofmann, Wayne Pettigrew, Vincent Sharps, William Peach for their friendship, partnership and support!

Preface

Sometimes we are so busy in life; we forget to live it. We also forget others have lived it and enjoyed it possibly a lot more because of the wisdom they acquired and used to live life at a whole new level.

Imagine back to when you were ten years old, and you just received the gift of the 50 book challenge? Ponder the extent of the knowledge placed in your hands. You may not have been ready for all that wisdom, but WOW, your world would now be open to new experiences and a new vocabulary to mold and program a future with possibilities of deciding how you want to play in life.

At a very young age of 10 years, we have already been awake for approximately 50,000 hours. 20 years = 100K hours, 30 years 150K hours, 40 years = 200K hours, and 50 years = 250,000 hours!

So to receive a challenge in one year to read one book a week for 1 hour is devoting 50 hours or 1% of your year to mastery of life wisdom in abundance, mindset, parenthood, relationships, wellness, and so much more.

When we devote 1 hour, it is equal to 1% of our waking hours.

The 80/20 rule states that 20% of our best efforts create 80% of our fruits of labor.

There is also a 90/10 rule, a 96/4 rule, and a 99/1 rule. Personally, I prefer the 99/1 rule of 1% causes a 99% impact of abundance and positivity.

As a collective, I propose a transformational mastermind where we give 1% to each other that provides 99% of our abundance... should you choose to accept it. Those that push away this valuable 1%, in essence, also push away 99% reward.

My desire in creating this book is for us to experience a 1% explosion of power, peace, and prosperity. After all, we are giving the very best recommendation of what drives and causes the best result in our life.

If you have lived 60 years, times 100 hours a week, that equates 72,000 hours to absorb several books of wisdom...CRAZY!!

I have met people that took an experience from reading only one book; they embraced it and became abundant.

My commitment to this challenge and the tens of thousands of people who accept it is that they reap this influx of abundant knowledge. Additionally, in reading the 50 book challenge, I stand that there will be a cause and effect that will shift humanity and the interest in Planetary Peace, Power, and Prosperity Legacy Foundation, Inc., (P4) by enrolling more ambassadors for this mission.

Inspiring people to be powerful is wonderful; giving them access to knowledge is the game-changer. :)

In closing, I will lead as an example of utilizing 1% of my time to read the books suggested in the challenge because it is the best we can give to each other what feeds the world HOPE.

Love,

Dr. Smiley

Introduction

The first book I was handed was a book on how to draw horses around the age of five. I may have received Dr. Seuss books and other children books that my mother read to me, but the one that changed my life was this 'How to Draw Horses' book. My parents probably purchased another thirty or forty drawing books on architecture, cartooning, drawing animals, people, etc. But spending what I remember to be about a year drawing hundreds of horses gave me the confidence and composition, motor skills (hand eye coordination), perspective, lighting (grey scale shading) to become a competent artist. As I evolved and read and studied more, I became a designer, illustrator and eventually a professional photographer.

I won several art grants to study art and science in college with a double major to become a medical illustrator. Although, I did not pursue the career, I read a huge array of books that inspired me to be a renaissance man/thinker.

The second book that I would identify changing my life significantly was 'The Adventures of Tom Sawyer' by Mark Twain. I marveled at Tom's ability to manipulate and leverage situations, which I later applied to my businesses, and marketing strategies. I believe this book planted the seed of entrepreneurism. I became a hustler. I mowed yards, shoveled snow, had a paper route for three years and really loved the concept of providing services and earning money in exchange for good customer service and work.

When I was roughly eighteen, my Uncle Bill (Meeker) gave me one of the best gifts an entrepreneur could ask for... *'The E-Myth'* By Michael Gerber. He saw my entrepreneur spirit and fed it with the perfect book. The E-Myth shared the reasons most businesses were unsuccessful and with those principles I have had a multitude of businesses that have lasted the test of time because of the principles I learned in this one book.

Several other books I purchased at age eighteen or there about, were *'Think and Grow Rich'* by Napoleon Hill, *'Raving Fans'* by Kenneth Blanchard, and *'Swim with The Sharks'* by Harvey McKay. These three books taught me about mindset, customer service, and having as many unique selling propositions as possible.

Over the years, I was introduced to Bob Burg, Timothy Ferris, Malcolm Gladwell, Seth Godin, John Maxwell, and many other amazing authors. This list of virtual mentors guided me to be a more confident businessman and leader.

This inspired me to finally accomplish writing and publishing a book in 2009, titled *'Becoming The Perfect Networker... Succeeding 1 Connection @ a Time'*. This book changed my life in so many ways, and ultimately gave me the writing bug to write seventeen more books to date and publish the work of at least twenty other authors.

My hope is to one day have a fifty book challenge with all the books I have published through Perfect Publishing (some of which are included in this book). If you have a book and believe it should be in *'The 50 Book Challenge'* series, please reach out to us at info@perfectpublishing.com.

We invite you to contribute titles of books that have made an impact on your life. We are developing a series from contributors like yourself and want to acknowledge YOU! Sign up today, be the first to contribute and receive bonus items we have planned for you at www.perfectpublishing. com

We are very committed to *'The 50 Book Challenge'* being a book that changes the world.

The 50 Book Challenge

DYLAN KING
DR. KEN ROCHON, JR.

Perfect Publishing

TheUmbrellaSyndicate.com

THE 50 BOOK CHALLENGE SYNOPSIS

Have you been browsed and browsed through books wondering what to buy? Have you missed the mark on a purchase of a book and felt sorely disappointed? Do you have loads of partially read books, because you lost interest and motivation? The 50 Book Challenge is just what you have been hoping for and will solve all the problems you experienced in the past. The first 50 Book Challenge is a smorgasbord of business, children, and personal development books. No matter your walk in life, if you are seeking the beauty of having balance in your personal and personal life, then this book is your answer to finding the path in many beautiful ways. A QR code is included with each book to connect you to Amazon to learn more quickly. You need to buy this today! You owe it to yourself and those you care about to take on the challenge that will change your life! YOU Will...• Discover a rich sense of accomplishment by reading books of successful leaders• Build habits of success in other areas of your life by finishing a challenge• Learn skills in all areas of your life that result in creating and completing goals• Increase your sense of purpose and joy in your life• Develop skills of decision-making, business savvy, time-management,communication and more. Implement these techniques your read from the diverse industry leaders in the 50Book Challenge and your personal and professional life will skyrocket. We recommend you take on this challenge with a friend or colleague or be a leader and start a reading club virtually or in your local area. And sign into our 50Book Challenge Community at www.perfectpublising.com today! My hope is that this book changes your life as much as the books featured inside this book changed mine. We are never the same person when we grow to think better and be a more positive and powerful human being.

The 50 Book Challenge For Champions

**KYLE MCGREGOR
DR. KEN ROCHON, JR.**

Perfect Publishing

TheUmbrellaSyndicate.com

THE 50 BOOK CHALLENGE FOR CHAMPIONS SYNOPSIS

Have you been browsed and browsed through books wondering what to buy? Have you missed the mark on a purchase of a book and felt sorely disappointed? Do you have loads of partially read books, because you lost interest and motivation? The 50 Book Challenge is just what you have been hoping for and will solve all the problems you experienced in the past. The first 50 Book Challenge is a smorgasbord of business, children, and personal development books. No matter your walk in life, if you are seeking the beauty of having balance in your personal and personal life, then this book is your answer to finding the path in many beautiful ways. A QR code is included with each book to connect you to Amazon to learn more quickly. You need to buy this today! You owe it to yourself and those you care about to take on the challenge that will change your life! YOU Will...• Discover a rich sense of accomplishment by reading books of successful leaders• Build habits of success in other areas of your life by finishing a challenge• Learn skills in all areas of your life that result in creating and completing goals• Increase your sense of purpose and joy in your life• Develop skills of decision-making, business savvy, time-management,communication and more. Implement these techniques your read from the diverse industry leaders in the 50Book Challenge and your personal and professional life will skyrocket. We recommend you take on this challenge with a friend or colleague or be a leader and start a reading club virtually or in your local area. And sign into our 50Book Challenge Community at www.perfectpublising.com today! My hope is that this book changes your life as much as the books featured inside this book changed mine. We are never the same person when we grow to think better and be a more positive and powerful human being.

The Absolute Spin

Music Defines the Moment

DR. KEN ROCHON, JR.
Perfect Publishing

TheUmbrellaSyndicate.com

KEN ROCHON is an international speaker, author, and highly acclaimed business professional. He is considered a renaissance spiritual leader, humanitarian and philanthropist who loves the arts and sciences.

THE ABSOLUTE SPIN SYNOPSIS

One of the biggest and most intangible elements to YOUR successful event is the entertainment, or more specifically, the mood created by the entertainment. A successful entertainment choice is one you and your guests will celebrate and enjoy thoroughly.

When it comes right down to it, the better the deejay is at reading the crowd and executing your vision, the more you will forget about time. Suddenly, your event will be over, with a full dance floor and you will exhale and think of what a great time you had. Surprised, you will say, "Is it over already?" That is the response a great deejay wants you to experience, because it means he/she did an outstanding job meeting YOUR expectations for your special occasion.

After 32 years in this industry, I have learned that there is a success formula that ensures consistent results and takes the guess work out of your entertainment decision. This easy to use formula that shows you a completely efficient way to logically guarantee that your guests will have the time of their life at your event.

The Art of Photobombing
Creating Engagement For Your Social Media

DR. KEN ROCHON, JR.
Perfect Publishing

TheUmbrellaSyndicate.com

THE ART OF PHOTOBOMBING SYNOPSIS

When I photographed my first photo bomb, I smiled. Then I looked at it later during post production and decided to keep it. I posted the photo in the event album and the rest is history.

That photo demonstrated a need to study how photo bombing could be used in a marketing context to increase engagement. This book gives lots of examples of successful photo bombing techniques that I hope will inspire you to jump into a photo in the future and have some fun while you add engagement to either a business event or family get together.

Art of Series

Art of Black and White

Art of Beauty – Ebony Edition

Art of Events

Art of Life

Art of Love

Art of Shoes & Sneakers

Art of Travel

Art of Weddings

DR. KEN ROCHON, JR.
Perfect Publishing

TheUmbrellaSyndicate.com

DR. KEN ROCHON, JR. "I have been blessed to see some remarkable things in life. Here is a small glimpse of what I have experienced.

The human spirit is love, and God has blessed me in so many ways to capture and Amplify the Goodness.

Almost every photo is a moment of tranquility, an unpredictable connection with life and the universe. I can remember having my finger resting on the button and feeling a sense of gratitude as I exhale and press down. I hear the shutter capture the energy and light and give thanks once again. My hope is it inspires you to share your dreams, use your camera, and tell your story."

Ken is lifetime entrepreneur, starting in his teen years, founding and delivering excellence with the award winning company Absolute Entertainment. He continues as a visionary and leader with companies and movements such as; The Perfect Networker, Live Loco Love Studio,The Perfect Publishing Ken has authored 17 books on diverse topics; children, linguistics, marketing, networking, and travel. He has published over 50 solo and compilation books. His current book 'Keep Smiling Shift Happens!' has caused a movement of celebrities and leaders to join in helping remind the world positivity, with just a simple smile, attracts positive power.The Umbrella Syndicate (TUS) was created, by Ken, with six elements represented by each segment of the umbrella that strategically and synergistically move the vision of a leader beyond their own minds eye. He studied strategies of leveraging like-minded and like hearted audiences to create these epic social proof campaigns for the leaders he chose to serve. Ken has created a formula that captures and catapults the message that wakes the world up with a positive frequency that inspires people to learn more.

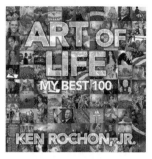

The Art of Life
My Best 100

DR. KEN ROCHON, JR.
Perfect Publishing

TheUmbrellaSyndicate.com

KEN ROCHON is an international speaker, author, and highly acclaimed business professional. He is considered a renaissance spiritual leader, humanitarian and philanthropist who loves the arts and sciences.

FATHER SON BOND SYNOPSIS

Ken is lifetime entrepreneur, starting in his teen years, founding and delivering excellence with the award winning company Absolute Entertainment. He continues as a visionary and leader with companies and movements such as; The Perfect Networker, Live Loco Love Studio,The Perfect Publishing Ken has authored 17 books on diverse topics; children, linguistics, marketing, networking, and travel. He has published over 50 solo and compilation books. His current book 'Keep Smiling Shift Happens!' has caused a movement of celebrities and leaders to join in helping remind the world positivity, with just a simple smile, attracts positive power.The Umbrella Syndicate (TUS) was created, by Ken, with six elements represented by each segment of the umbrella that strategically and synergistically move the vision of a leader beyond their own minds eye. He studied strategies of leveraging like-minded and like hearted audiences to create these epic social proof campaigns for the leaders he chose to serve. Ken has created a formula that captures and catapults the message that wakes the world up with a positive frequency that inspires people to learn more.

Be the Smartest Kid in the Room

DR. KEN 'SMILEY' ROCHON, JR.

Perfect Publishing

TheUmbrellaSyndicate.com

KEN 'K3' ROCHON, III is a 7-year-old boy, Game Changer – Leader. He recently was published as an author, and he is an expert in children's jokes.

BE THE SMARTEST KID IN THE ROOM SYNOPSIS

Want to be the Smartest Kid in the Room? I sure did! And I wanted my son to be as well. But not in a way of feeling pressure or stress, but because of confidence and the joy of learning.

This book is a beautiful mix of amazing facts and trivia from all the important subjects. This information will prepare you for game shows, and spelling bees, and the go to person for answers and solutions.

The person with the most knowledge is someone that is sought after because they bring solutions and value to opportunities and relationships.

The best thing about being the Smartest Kid in the room, is you can help others be smart too. What better way to make friends.

If you know anyone not having fun in life, give them this book, it will change their life. It is only fair... it changed yours. So you become a hero for someone because they were inspired by your generosity and love for knowledge.

Knowledge and learning is fun when it is a game. The smarter you become, the more you realize life is a game too... the more fun you have, the more you know... and the more you know... the more fun you have.

Becoming The Perfect Networker...

Succeeding 1 Connection at a Time

DR. KEN ROCHON, JR.

Perfect Publishing

TheUmbrellaSyndicate.com

KEN ROCHON is an international speaker, author, and highly acclaimed business professional. He is considered a renaissance spiritual leader, humanitarian and philanthropist who loves the arts and sciences.

After losing his mom to Alzheimer's Disease in 2008, he searched for meaning and purpose in his life. He prayed for a sign that would allow him to dedicate his life to service and utilize his skillsets to amplify leaders making a positive impact in the world.

His gift to amplify (market viral campaigns on social media) the messages of authors, speakers, and leaders is referred to as a game changer in the social media world. He studied strategies of leveraging like-minded and like hearted audiences to create these epic social proof campaigns for the leaders he chose to serve. Ken is invited to some of the biggest and influential international events He delivers powerful messages on how to create a catalyst effect between the power of influence and visual story telling through photography to cause social proof viral campaigns that benefit everyone. A viral campaign markets the message of the event or a leader and in essence wakes the world up with a positive frequency that inspires people to learn more about the event, the leaders, the speakers and sponsors.

He is a specialist in creating 'Social Proof Viral Campaigns' for some of the top events, leaders, non-profits and organizations. His ability to see the vision of a leader, and capture the essence of the human spirit, cause the perception of the vision to become a reality.

He has authored 17 books on a multitude of topics to include children, linguistics, marketing, networking, and travel. His current book 'Keep Smiling... Shift Happens!' has caused a movement of celebrities and leaders to want to join in helping remind the world positivity attracts positive power.

Ken has contributed his unique skills and art to hundreds of events he and his company support and market each year. His desire to inspire living a purpose driven life caused him to create The Umbrella Syndicate to support authors, leaders and speakers.

Ken loves to travel and recently accomplished one of his goals of experiencing over 100 countries. Ken's favorite place to travel is back home. His son Kenny is the light of his life.

BECOMING THE PERFECT NETWORKER... **SYNOPSIS**

This business networking book teaches offline and online networking. How to make connections and turn them into relationships that produce income and opportunities. How to be successful in social networking as well as explanations of the programs available on PerfectNetworker website. Philosophical approaches to networking that create results that lead to a balanced life.

The Centurion World Traveller Game

(Knocking out your bucket list)

Ken Rochon, Jr.

The Centurion World Traveller Game

DR. KEN ROCHON, JR.
Perfect Publishing

TheUmbrellaSyndicate.com

KEN ROCHON is an international speaker, author, and highly acclaimed business professional. He is considered a renaissance spiritual leader, humanitarian and philanthropist who loves the arts and sciences.

THE CENTURION WORLD TRAVELLER GAME SYNOPSIS

My hope is to inspire you to connect with the world. Many of us including myself fall into a trap of believing we are only able to do so much with the money, and time we have. It is a dangerous trap, because it becomes our reality. The purpose of this book is to make life a game… and you win points the more you play.

If someone told me eight years ago that I would be writing a book on how to travel to 100 countries (Become a Centurion World Traveller), I would have bet against it. I hadn't been to even one country outside the U.S.A. since I was twelve years old.

This book not only gives you an education on what is in the world to experience, but it gives you a real plan that is manageable. Travel has an amazing ability to expand your horizons and break through previously believed limits or hurdles. I promise you that when you take a taste of the world, you will fall in love with it… because the people you encounter will show you that we have more in common that we may have believed.

The Customer Experience

CHRISTOFF J. WEIHMAN

ASPIRE Enterprises

THE CUSTOMER EXPERIENCE SYNOPSIS

It All Begins & Ends with... The Customer Experience *Have you ever Wondered what it would be like if All your Customers Loved the way you Serve them & Constantly Raved about You to Others? *Can You Imagine if You had the Perfect Team, Delivering Amazing Customer Service, Consistently, to your Appreciative, Valued Customers? *And How would You Feel if your Business was Booming, because the Experience your Customers have when they Engage Your Business was Above and Beyond Anything that they Could Experience Elsewhere? That's what 'The Customer Experience' will do for you and Your Business

"This book is a great read! The concepts Christoff offers about energy and customer service are spot on. I believe this book is the key to helping companies create a culture for their employees that takes the customer experience to another level that will show up on the bottom line. A rising tide floats all boats!" James Dentley, International Speaker, Business Strategist & Author of The Five Frequencies of High Performance

Diagrams

DR. KEN ROCHON, JR.
Perfect Publishing

TheUmbrellaSyndicate.com

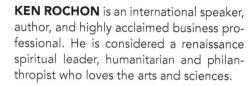

KEN ROCHON is an international speaker, author, and highly acclaimed business professional. He is considered a renaissance spiritual leader, humanitarian and philanthropist who loves the arts and sciences.

DIAGRAMS SYNOPSIS

A Picture is worth a thousand words…

A Diagram is worth a million … dollars and / or words. Diagrams explain difficult concepts in the simplest terms. Removing verbose explanations of the how to create the result and the operational workings of why laws of life behave and create outcomes we either want or do not want.

Since this book was written for children and adults, it only makes sense that it must entertain. Thus, there are diagrams of humor interjected randomly into the book to keep this book fun as much as it is enlightening.

Life is a work in progress, and so are diagrams and this book. I challenge you to submit diagrams for future editions that will awaken the mind and soul with how life works (better with diagrams).

Have an enlightening and joyous journey through 50 years of analyzing how life works.

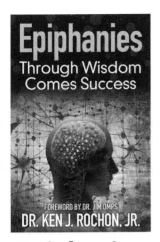

Epiphanies
Through Wisdom
Comes Success

DR. KEN ROCHON, JR.
Perfect Publishing

TheUmbrellaSyndicate.com

KEN ROCHON is an international speaker, author, and highly acclaimed business professional. He is considered a renaissance spiritual leader, humanitarian and philanthropist who loves the arts and sciences.

FATHER SON BOND SYNOPSIS

50 years of living on this planet gives you a degree of wisdom you may wish to download and share. Some people are lifelong readers, some are personal development junkies, some world travelers, and some become rather street smart through the study of communication, psychology and survival. This book is a download of all the knowledge I wanted to share in my dissertation for a PhD in Philosophy and Entreprenology... the study of how Entrepreneurs succeed and what to avoid preventing inevitable failure in most cases.

I wish I had this book when I was starting my journey as an entrepreneur at age 18. But some of the life lessons I learned needed to be learned to test my persistence in being successful. This is the perfect gift if you want to accelerate your success and increase your chance of making a difference with your mission, vision and dreams.

After visiting over 100 countries, studying a dozen different languages and running six different businesses, I have a lot to share that may help you think bigger, be more impactful and avoid mistakes I was fortunate enough to survive. partnerships that work, how to leverage effort and opportunities and most importantly how to create a legacy for your life.

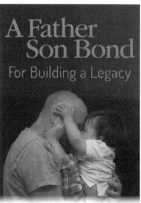

Ken Rochon, Jr.

Father Son Bond

DR. KEN ROCHON, JR.
Perfect Publishing

TheUmbrellaSyndicate.com

KEN ROCHON is an international speaker, author, and highly acclaimed business professional. He is considered a renaissance spiritual leader, humanitarian and philanthropist who loves the arts and sciences.

FATHER SON BOND SYNOPSIS

Building a legacy is our footprint on this planet that we made a difference. This book provides 100 life lessons that I've learned either from my father or mentors. The gift in this book is that the early and better you learn these lessons, the more abundance, happier and successful you will be.

This book is my most important work, but it serves to communicate love and wisdom to my son regardless of whether I am here with him or not. We are never truly prepared to say goodbye to the ones we love, but the more messages of love we leave, the more our life continues to impact our loved ones.

I don't have a big family, but I want my son to have everything he wants in life. I want him to understand the being a good person is the best training one could have to be a great future father. That is when I truly know I was successful.

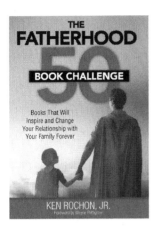

The Fatherhood Book Guide...

50 Book Challenge for Fathers

WAYNE PETTIGREW
DR. KEN ROCHON, JR.
Perfect Publishing

TheUmbrellaSyndicate.com

THE FATHERHOOD BOOK GUIDE...
SYNOPSIS

If you want to be the best father in the world to your biggest gifts in the world, then this book is an introduction to over 50 authors and their books one advice, ideas, strategies for bringing up a son or daughter you are connected to at the highest level.

This book will help you navigate to the information you need for the stage your child is going through in life. Having the answers is like having the right key to open a lock. You will be empowered to make a difference and enjoy the process to the fullest.

Most elderly people say their biggest regret is not spending more time with their children and family, this book will make every minute count... with a lot less regrets.

Five Star Reviews

**DR. KEN ROCHON, JR.,
RON HOWARD, TREVOR
HOWARD, TROY
HOWARD**

Perfect Publishing

FIVE STAR REVIEWS SYNOPSIS

In this high tech, high touch world, it is easy to get lost in an abyss of information. With that, it is harder than ever to stand out and be heard, or noticed. When you are playing full out and the evidence of social proof is not shown online that you are doing significant things in this world, then you are not properly leveraging what you are doing. This book will show you the secrets and strategies for putting together a social proof marketing campaign that could 10X your business. If you are satisfying clients everyday, there is no reason why you are not memorializing these accomplishments through reviews systems. This will ultimately prove you are the best person/business a potential client should consider working with because you consistently show professionalism and value. Whether you are an author, baker, banker, deejay, leader, realtor, speaker or inventor, this book will show you how to capture, post, promote and secure sales funnels with your 5 Star Reviews. And ultimately, when you follow this system you will find that 5 Star Reviews really do equal 5 $tar $ales!!

"A well written, not so common sense guide for the entire service and hospitality industry. It is meant to be consumed page by enlightening page. Bon Appétit" - Rick Moonen

Getting to WOW!

Everybody WINS with 5 Star Service

CHRISTOFF J. WEIHMAN

Getting to WOW!

Everybody WINS with 5 Star Service

CHRISTOFF J. WEIHMAN

ASPIRE Enterprises

CHRISTOFF J WEIHMAN I have worked in the hotel & restaurant industry on & off since I was 15 years old. I have a passion for excellence in Service & Hospitality. I've served-as a server, bartender, wine sales rep, catering sales manager, event planner & banquet service manager. Regardless of the type of restaurant, Excellent Service must always be the goal. "You can have the most beautiful décor; relaxing, wonderful ambience; creative, inspired food with the freshest ingredients prepared by an amazing, James Beard Award winning chef but if the Service & Hospitality is not on point & given equal focus & attention, then that establishment will not succeed. The servers are the unsung heroes of this business."

GETTING TO WOW! SYNOPSIS

This Book has your name written all over it *If you work in the Service & Hospitality industry in any capacity... *If you want to up your game of Service and you want to learn how to consistently WOW! your guests... *If you are a seasoned professional in the industry but have lost your spark along the way and want to get it back... *If you own or manage a restaurant, hotel, casino, resort & you want to equip your team to deliver WOW! service, create loyal guests & increase your profits... *If you want to excel in the restaurant industry or any other, where you serve customers, clients, patrons or guests & you want to deliver the WOW!.. then, Getting to WOW! Everybody WINS with 5 Star Service is for you!

Keep Smiling ... Shift Happens

DR. KEN ROCHON, JR.

Perfect Publishing

TheUmbrellaSyndicate.com

KEN ROCHON is an international speaker, author, and highly acclaimed business professional. He is considered a renaissance spiritual leader, humanitarian and philanthropist who loves the arts and sciences.

KEEP SMILING...SHIFT HAPPENS SYNOPSIS

A smile is the most powerful expression on earth! It is an expression of connection, positivity, and even love.

When we experience a challenging day, it often changes our focus to what is wrong and attracts more of the same feelings trapping us in a mindset of aloneness, negativity, and scarcity. The only way to break this mindset is to shift. This book shares two beautiful stories of the power of a smile and hundreds of photos and quotes from authors, leaders, speakers and celebrities. These people were chosen because they influence us to feel better.

Just like a child's laugh is contagious, so is a smile. This book will help you create a better state of mind to be the powerful person you are.

A smile radiates positive energy, and this book will help you attract what you and everyone ultimately wants in life... Happiness! Many would agree that true success in life is a reflection of how many smiles you have.

Share your smiles on www.facebook.com/KeepSmilingMovement

KEN 'DR. SMILEY' ROCHON, JR., PhD

Keep Smiling

Influencer Birthday Color Edition

DR. JANET SMITH WARFIELD
DR. KEN ROCHON, JR.

Perfect Publishing

TheUmbrellaSyndicate.com

KEN ROCHON is an international speaker, author, and highly acclaimed business professional. He is considered a renaissance spiritual leader, humanitarian and philanthropist who loves the arts and sciences.

KEEP SMILING INFLUENCER BIRTHDAY SYNOPSIS

A smile is the most powerful expression on earth! It is an expression of connection, positivity, and even love.

When we experience a challenging day, it often changes our focus to what is wrong and attracts more of the same feelings trapping us in a mindset of aloneness, negativity, and scarcity. The only way to break this mindset is to shift. This book shares two beautiful stories of the power of a smile and hundreds of photos and quotes from authors, leaders, speakers and celebrities. These people were chosen because they influence us to feel better.

Just like a child's laugh is contagious, so is a smile. This book will help you create a better state of mind to be the powerful person you are.

A smile radiates positive energy, and this book will help you attract what you and everyone ultimately wants in life... Happiness! Many would agree that true success in life is a reflection of how many smiles you have.

Share your smiles on www.facebook.com/KeepSmilingMovement

Keep Smiling
Dose of Hope
DR. KEN ROCHON, JR.
Perfect Publishing

TheUmbrellaSyndicate.com

KEN ROCHON is an international speaker, author, and highly acclaimed business professional. He is considered a renaissance spiritual leader, humanitarian and philanthropist who loves the arts and sciences.

KEEP SMILING DOSE OF HOPE SYNOPSIS

A "D.O.S.E. of HOPE" is what everyone needs. Fortunately, we have been given a gift, a natural D.O.S.E. (Dopamine, Oxytocin, Serotonin, & Endorphins) of chemicals, neurotransmitters, within our brains that are induced by smiles. Smiles awaken our spirit to live a life of J.O.Y. We carefully chose Heroes of HOPE, who exemplify living a life they created through faith, hope, patience, and persistence. No matter what page you open to in this mini cube of HOPE, you will find a leader with a big heart. You will see you are not alone. The authors may share similar challenges that only hope and action could resolve. The bigger you play in life, the bigger the challenges, and the bigger the reward. This journey is not about money, work, and worry. Instead, it is about abundance, creation, happiness & joy. Shift your life with a D.O.S.E. of HOPE & Keep Smiling

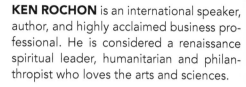

Keep Smiling

**Transformational
Leaders Color
Edition**

**DR. JANET SMITH
WARFIELD
DR. KEN ROCHON, JR.**

Perfect Publishing

TheUmbrellaSyndicate.com

KEN ROCHON is an international speaker, author, and highly acclaimed business professional. He is considered a renaissance spiritual leader, humanitarian and philanthropist who loves the arts and sciences.

KEEP SMILING TRANSFORMATIONAL LEADERS SYNOPSIS

One of the biggest accomplishments in life is leaving a legacy. The challenge is creating a life that matters so much, that you have something significant to contribute to the world after you are gone. The authors in this book I have met, and I am moved by their drive and human spirit. They live a leadership lifestyle and they download their knowledge with the intention of contributing to the world. I am proud to showcase who they are and what legacy they have created for you.

A smile is the most powerful expression on earth! It is an expression of connection, positivity, and even love. Just like a child's laugh is contagious, so is a smile. This book will help you create a better state of mind to be the powerful person you are. A smile radiates positive energy, and this book will help you attract what you and everyone ultimately wants in life... Happiness! Many would agree that true success in life is a reflection of how many smiles you have.

Share your smiles on www.facebook.com/KeepSmilingMovement

Kenny's Favorite Jokes

Cracken You Up
KENNY (K3) ROCHON, III & DADDY

Perfect Publishing

TheUmbrellaSyndicate.com

KEN 'K3' ROCHON, III is a 7-year-old boy, Game Changer – Leader. He recently was published as an author, and he is an expert in children's jokes.

KENNY'S FAVORITE JOKES SYNOPSIS

This is my book and it is funny, and if you laugh, you should buy one. And if you like people to laugh you should buy one for every person you know. They will like you more and will probably even hug you. Laughter is the best medicine for a life of happiness and joy. I always say, 'A day without sunshine is like ... night'. My Daddy thinks I am one of the funniest people in our home. He should know, I live with him and I know humor like the back of my hand. If fact I would say I know humor so much, that I consider myself not only humorous, but actually hysterical. Thanks for supporting future comedians. For every dollar I raise for this book, I will put it in my bank... and you can take that to the bank... I mean my bank... that will save me a trip. Well my hands are getting tired writing,my fingers are tired of typing, so tha must mean this back cover is done. That's All Folks!

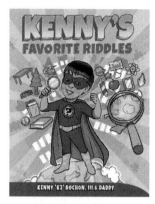

Kenny's Favorite Riddles

KENNY (K3) ROCHON, III & DADDY

Perfect Publishing

TheUmbrellaSyndicate.com

KEN 'K3' ROCHON, III is a 7-year-old boy, Game Changer – Leader. He recently was published as an author, and he is an expert in children's jokes.

KENNY'S FAVORITE RIDDLES SYNOPSIS

With this book, I wanted to take a more in-depth and more serious look at humor regarding riddles and how riddles develop and inspire thinking outside the box. As you may know, the most successful people in the world are out-of-the-box thinkers. To solve riddles, you look for clues that exercise your brain to be more creative, which allows you to solve riddles and problems. The better you are at solving problems, the more valuable you become to society and the world. Most problem-solvers are great at puzzles, riddles, and word games.

When you master the riddles in this book, you, in essence, become a person who could create positive changes with a new way of approaching world problems and challenges. Just like anything in life, the more you practice, the more you master.
I am excited for you as you learn how to be more confident in solving riddles and future problems. Just think, you owe your future stardom to this book. If this book changes your life by improving your brain power and confidence as much as I believe it will, I only ask you to invest in a book for everyone you love, so they can become world-class problem-solvers. If you don't want anyone else to be as smart as you, I recommend you read this book, master it, then destroy it. Leaving any evidence of this brilliance could generate competition to cause the world to be a better place.

Kenny's Favorite Science Facts & Trivia

Be The Smartest Kid In The Room!
KENNY (K3) ROCHON, III & DADDY
Perfect Publishing

TheUmbrellaSyndicate.com

KEN 'K3' ROCHON, III is a 7-year-old boy, Game Changer – Leader. He recently was published as an author, and he is an expert in children's jokes.

KENNY'S FAVORITE THINGS TO KNOW SYNOPSIS

A child is a sponge, so let them soak up knowledge that gives them confidence and a desire to continue to learn. When you feel like the smartest kid in the room, you embrace learning as if it were a daily regimen of nutrition for the brain.

This book gamifies the experience of knowledge with fun facts of science. Watch your child stump adults and relish in their acumen as a future scholar and world leader.

If only I had this book when I was young... but you are never to old to learn. Joining your child in the journey of learning is transforming the priorities of the family focus and ultimately the family bond.

It is said we use 5 percent of our brain. This book will stimulate the brain and cause a ripple effect in conversations, friendships and ultimately career choices.

Live a life of learning and you will live a life you love!

Kenny's
Favorite
Things to
Know

KENNY (K3) ROCHON, III
& DADDY

Perfect Publishing

TheUmbrellaSyndicate.com

KEN 'K3' ROCHON, III is a 7-year-old boy, Game Changer – Leader. He recently was published as an author, and he is an expert in children's jokes.

KENNY'S FAVORITE THINGS TO KNOW SYNOPSIS

Little did Leonardo Da Vinci know he would inspire the Vitruvian Boy. The symbol of balance and knowledge in the arts and sciences.

This book will awaken your child's desire to engage, grow, learn and value knowledge.

After all the more your child knows, they more they will grow to be future confident leaders. Perhaps they would love to share their favorite things to know and have their very own book... to help them achieve, believe and create a life from their dreams and imagination.

Kenny guarantees this knowledge will help you be more successful. This is the most important book he has published because it encompasses the best of the best in what you want to know as a young leader.

Kenny's Favorite Trivia

**KENNY (K3) ROCHON, III
& DADDY**

Perfect Publishing

TheUmbrellaSyndicate.com

KEN 'K3' ROCHON, III is a 7-year-old boy, Game Changer – Leader. He recently was published as an author, and he is an expert in children's jokes. e.

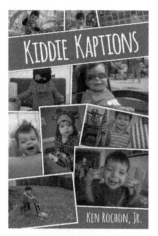

Kiddie Kaptions

DR. KEN ROCHON, JR.

Perfect Publishing

TheUmbrellaSyndicate.com

KEN ROCHON is an international speaker, author, and highly acclaimed business professional. He is considered a renaissance spiritual leader, humanitarian and philanthropist who loves the arts and sciences.

KIDDIE KAPTIONS SYNOPSIS

Children bring the child out in us. I believe without babies and children, our cynicism would grow with age and this is God's way of bringing us back to our loving soul. I am a more gentle and patient person with Kenny reminding me how precious life is. Kids are entertaining, and many humorous moments go undocumented I try to spend at least five minutes a day documenting Kenny's growth and sense of humor. He loves to laugh and has been witnessed spontaneously cracking up...which is Kentagious to say the least. This is the first version and my hope is to inspire others to contribute their best captions and cause others to submit their favorite times with their children.

Make a Book Move a Book Book a SALE

DR. KEN ROCHON, JR., SARAH COOLIDGE, AL GRANGER, KEITH LEON, ANN MCINDOO

Perfect Publishing

MAKE A BOOK MOVE A BOOK BOOK A SALE SYNOPSIS

Five well-known book experts come together to illustrate the three most important steps you need to take to produce your book and move your business to the next level. If you have not yet written a book, or the book you wrote has put you in the book storage business, or you don't know how to use your book to explode your sales, this book is for you! This step-by-step guide will help you create your ideal book (and other products) so you can make a real, profitable impact with your ideas In this book you will learn: • The best and easiest ways to write your book • How to create and produce a book you'll be proud of • Why a book is the best business card you can have • How to use your book to skyrocket your business growth • Three mistakes business owners often make to scare potential clients away.

Making Friends Around the World

DR. KEN ROCHON, JR.
Perfect Publishing

TheUmbrellaSyndicate.com

KEN ROCHON is an international speaker, author, and highly acclaimed business professional. He is considered a renaissance spiritual leader, humanitarian and philanthropist who loves the arts and sciences.

MAKING FRIENDS AROUND THE WORLD SYNOPSIS

A delightful way for children and adults to learn 10 of the most popular languages in the world. Whether you travel or want your children to be more globally aware and competitive in an ever changing world. This book makes learning languages fun.

The No-Nonsense Book on Nonsense

DR. KEN ROCHON, JR.
Perfect Publishing

TheUmbrellaSyndicate.com

KEN ROCHON is an international speaker, author, and highly acclaimed business professional. He is considered a renaissance spiritual leader, humanitarian and philanthropist who loves the arts and sciences.

THE NO-NONSENSE BOOK ON NONSENSE SYNOPSIS

Nonsense is fun, and keeps us from taking life so serious, but when nonsense is taken seriously, ironically life tends to not be as fun. For example, if you believe nonsense, you are typically allowing yourself to be convinced that nonsense is your guiding light. 'If you enjoyed this book half as much as I did writing it, then I enjoyed myself two times more than you.' ~ Ken Rochon Where do I start? Does it matter? This book is nonsense! But if there is any part of this book that should be less nonsense, it should be the introduction. But if I write an introduction without nonsense, then I am being a hypocrite on at least some level since the back of the book states this book is 100% nonsense. A regrettable commitment to have made, but what can I do? You either give 100% to something or you make up that you gave more than 100%... like 110% and really show the nonsense you are believing is possible.

THE **PERFECT**
NETW★RK-OUT
BALANCING, CREATING & LIVING
WEALTH + WELLNESS

KEN ROCHON
SHANNON BROWN • DONNA GALLAGHER • DR. DONNA GOLDSTEIN
JACQUELINE LARSEN • KAY LOUGHREY • SHIRLEY LUU
MICHAEL MADFIS • MARCIA MERRILL
DR. SAMMY NOUMBISSI • DR. JUDY STAVELEY • BECCA TEBON

Perfect NetworkOut

Balancing, Creating & Living Wealth + Wellness

DR. KEN ROCHON, JR.
Perfect Publishing

TheUmbrellaSyndicate.com

SHANNON BROWN, DONNA GALLAGHER, DR. DONNA GOLDSTEIN, JACQUELINE LARSEN, KAY LOUGHREY, SHIRLEY LUU, MICHAEL MADFIS • MARCIA MERRILL, DR. SAMMY NOUMBISSI, TRINA RICE, DR. JUDY STAVELEY, BECCA TEBON

PERFECT NETWORKOUT SYNOPSIS

This book is about the marriage of wealth and wellness. If they are not operating in harmony in your life, this book addresses key ways to integrate and create a life you love. We all love to be with positive people, and when you have wealth and wellness, you increase your positive and powerful energy, which acts like a magnet to bring you even more positive and powerful connections, which ultimately leads to you experiencing more abundance. This book delivers the information needed and the actions you will want to take to create a more enjoyable and meaningful journey. The great news is that each of us is in control of our abundance, happiness and wellness. We just need to choose to adopt new ways of being.

The Perfect Office... A Home Away From Home

Perfect Publishing

DR. KEN ROCHON, JR., KIMMOLY RICE-OGLETREE, KEN ROCHON JR., PATSY ANDERSON, GEORGANNE CAMMARATA, BRAD BERGERSEN, KIM WESLEY, CARA MICHELE NETHER, DEANA GEPPI, MARCIA MERRELL, ALEXANDER MOROZOV, AL GRANGER BRAD MAY, PATRICK AHERN, AUSTIN DUNCAN, MIKE CHASMAN, KIRBY SPENCER, MICK & TARA CARBO TERRY WEIGEL

THE PERFECT OFFICE... A HOME AWAY FROM HOME SYNOPSIS

A book designed to inspire you to step up your game in business. This book is about 17 home based businesses that joined forces and created a strategic alliance that allowed each partner to experience a better way of doing business. Each partner brings a strength to the office and through master mind techniques, leveraging, creating events, and products, each business has strengthened it's profitability and productivity.

QUiCK
Solutions
to World
Problems

DR. KEN ROCHON, JR.
Perfect Publishing

TheUmbrellaSyndicate.com

KEN ROCHON is an international speaker, author, and highly acclaimed business professional. He is considered a renaissance spiritual leader, humanitarian and philanthropist who loves the arts and sciences.

QUICK SOLUTIONS TO WORLD PROBLEMS SYNOPSIS

This book drills down and addresses world problems in a no nonsense way.

Estimates of the total overall costs of substance abuse in the United States, including productivity and health- and crime-related costs, exceed $600 billion annually. This includes approximately $193 billion for illicit drugs,1 $193 billion for tobacco,2 and $235 billion for alcohol.3 As staggering as these numbers are, they do not fully describe the breadth of destructive public health and safety implications of drug abuse and addiction, such as family disintegration, loss of employment, failure in school, domestic violence, and child abuse. - Drugabuse.gov

We can go back to the beginning of time and learn Bullying, gossip, inequality, and judging are just some forms of discrimination that has held back mankind. The reason we argue, fight and go to war is because we don't know how to appreciate differences. This book takes on a problem that if unsolved could cause the extinction of our species.

The Chemistry & Psychology of Happiness

KEN ROCHON, JR.

Science of Smiles
The Chemistry & Psychology of Happiness

DR. KEN ROCHON, JR.

Perfect Publishing

TheUmbrellaSyndicate.com

SCIENCE OF SMILES SYNOPSIS

Want PROOF YOU CAN LIVE HAPPIER, LONGER with MORE ABUNDANCE and LOVE in YOUR LIFE?

You have just picked up the book that could bring YOU more JOY than any other book on the planet, because the focus of the book is... YOUR JOY!

So many people are working through life joyless letting life pass them by. They complain how hard life is and wish they could be HAPPY or at least be at PEACE.

This book gives YOU PROOF that JOY, HAPPINESS, and PEACE are a POSSIBILITY by CHOICE through exercises, habits, and mindset shifts that are much EASIER than you can imagine.

This book is all about reflecting PROOF that SMILES are God's GIFT to humanity to express ACCEPTANCE, AFFINITY, and LOVE!

IMAGINE YOUR LIFE and a WORLD of HAPPINESS... it starts with people

What BETTER GIFT can YOU GIVE the PEOPLE YOU LOVE then making YOURSELF the HAPPIEST by seeing the PEOPLE YOU LOVE being HAPPY?

The Science of Smiles...it's MORE than a book, it's the ACCESS to the LIFE GIFT of LOVE through the biochemical POWER OF SMILES!

Shift
Change Your Words, Change Your World

JANET SMITH WARFIELD

Word Sculptures
Publishing, L.P.

SHIFT SYNOPSIS

Shift is a creative tool for expanding consciousness. Through thought-provoking questions, stories, and poetry, *Shift* draws out new ways of thinking about old challenges. Its purpose is to bring powerful peace to the listener and thus, powerful peace to the planet, one listener at a time. The audiobook is unique in using words, music, and sound effects to look at words, meanings, human perception, emotions, and actions. Its words are not Truth; they are catalysts helping listeners find their own truths.

The audiobook was produced by a wonderful team: John Mahoney of Ravenpheat Productions, LLC; Norma-Jean Strickland (female voice); and Sule Greg Wilson (male voice). We had a blast doing it! I gave John, Norma-Jean, and Sule free reign in deciding who would read what and how they would do it! John's sound effects were delightful. The audiobook has a much richer character than reading words on a flat piece of paper.

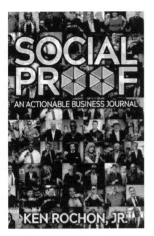

Social Proof
The Who, What, Why, Where, When, and How

DR. KEN ROCHON, JR.
Perfect Publishing

TheUmbrellaSyndicate.com

SOCIAL PROOF **SYNOPSIS**

Anyone can say that they're good at what they do, but sometimes that's not always the case. It's easy for any person to say, "Hey, I'm the best person for the job," especially on social media, where they can just easily type those words in their post even when it's not true. People want to work with those they know, like, and trust, those who are authentic and fulfill their promises. So, if you really are good at what you do, how can you prove that to other people? What do you do to make people know, like, and trust you? Is your proof consistent and congruent in your campaigns?

Social proof is a powerful tool that can help you gain and garner social power and influence. You just need to know how to get it and use it the right way in order to leverage yourself, because the truth is this: social proof works both ways, it can prove that you're either good or bad, which is why it's important to remember that you need to show consistency and congruency in both your offline and online lives. Social proof, if done correctly, can propel you to the top so you can stand out from the crowd.

Social Proof is part of the THiNKaha series, whose slim and handy books contain 140 well-thought-out AHA messages. Increase your online influence by picking up AHAthat, and easily share quotes from this book on Twitter, Facebook, LinkedIn, and Google+ via this link: http://aha.pub/SocialProof

Umbrella Marketing
Amplify Your Message!

DR. KEN ROCHON, JR.
Perfect Publishing

TheUmbrellaSyndicate.com

KEN ROCHON is an international speaker, author, and highly acclaimed business professional. He is considered a renaissance spiritual leader, humanitarian and philanthropist who loves the arts and sciences.

UMBRELLA MARKETING SYNOPSIS

This book was put together by professional, talented, proven entrepreneurs, not only willing, but eager, to share their secrets, tips, shortcuts and tried-and-true methods on how to best market and amplify your brand, logo, website—any dream you desire to turn into a reality—by online and offline networking and marketing.

This book is for you if …

- You're curious about all of these terms you've been hearing on a daily basis – branding, logos, fan pages, SEO, social media, going viral, etc.
- You have a company, you're great at networking, but need some advice on how to combine your online and offline marketing.
- You've just set up your website or put your business page on Facebook and have no idea how to get people to visit.
- You think you've done everything right, but you're still not getting listed on the first page, above-the-fold.
- You have a great idea or message and you need to know the fastest, most cost-effective way to get it out there.

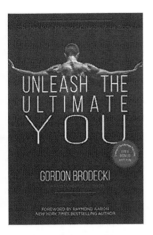

Unleash The Ultimate YOU

Change Your Mindset, Change Your Body

GORDON BRODECKI

Independently published

UNLEASH THE ULTIMATE YOU SYNOPSIS

Tapping into the power of your mindset, Gordon sets you on the path to becoming the 'Ultimate You', no matter what life throws your way. With decades of experience in physical training and bodybuilding coaching, Gordon also tackles how your relationship with food and exercise can be sabotaging your efforts to create long-lasting change.

With Unleash the Ultimate You: Change Your Mindset, Change Your Body, Gordon offers the knowledge and tips to get you on a path of lifelong physical fitness, tailored to your personal goals, thus allowing you to live your best life!

ART OF SERIES
https://we.tl/t-gpKJtSe7AW

CHILDREN'S & KENNY'S BOOKS
https://we.tl/t-cJz2RFKqGe

HOPE PROJECT (D.O.S.E. / DOPE)
https://we.tl/t-XVeeJZTANO

KEN'S BOOKS
https://rb.gy/uso5ch

KEEP SMILING BOOKS
http://rebrand.ly/dbitd5o

More Books From

    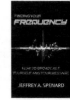

www.PerfectPublishing.com